Treasury of Aesop's Fables

Treasury of
AESOP'S FABLES

Illustrated by THOMAS BEWICK

Together with The *Life of Æsop*,

by OLIVER GOLDSMITH

AVENEL BOOKS
NEW YORK

51711321X
Library Of Congress Catalog Card Number: 73-76024
This edition published by Avenel Books
a division of Crown Publishers, Inc.
One Park Avenue
New York, New York 10016
k l m n o p q
Manufactured in the United States of America

LIFE OF ÆSOP

by Oliver Goldsmith

ÆSOP, according to the best accounts, was a native of Phrygia, a province of the *Lesser Asia*, and born in the city Cotiæum. He was a person of a remarkable genius, and extraordinary character; for though he was born a slave, by the assistance of his genius and virtue only, he procured his own emancipation. By his sage counsels and judicious advice he directed his countrymen to measures that secured their liberty, and by a single Fable baffled the tyrannical projects of Crœsus, King of Lydia. The most part of writers agree that his person was but unseemly, though there are some of a contrary opinion. It is probable that he was of a low and diminutive stature, though agreeable in his complexion, and polite in his manners. It is, however, certain that he had a great soul, and was endowed with extraordinary mental qualifications; his moral character approached to a degree of perfection to which very few have attained. He appears to have had a true sense of morality and a just discernment of right and wrong; his perceptions and feelings of truth were scrupulously nice, and the smallest deviation from rectitude impressed his mind with the greatest antipathy. No considerations of private interest could warp his inclinations so as to seduce him from the paths of virtue; his principles were stedfast and determined, and truly habitual. He never employed his great wisdom to serve the purposes of cunning; but, with an uncommon exactness, made his understanding a servant to truth. Historians have given many instances of his wit and shrewdness, which were always employed in the service of virtue, philanthropy, and benevolence.

It cannot well be ascertained who were his parents, though some have affirmed that his father was a shepherd. He himself was undoubtedly a slave; his first master was an Athenian, whose name was Caresias. At Athens he learned the Greek language in perfection, and acquired a taste for writing moral instructions, in the way of Fables, which was then the prevailing mode

of teaching morals in Attica. His Fables are al-
legorical stories, delivered with an air of fiction,
under various personifications, to convey truth
to the mind in an agreeable manner. By telling
a story of a *Lion*, *Dog*, or a *Wolf*, the Fabulist
describes the manners and characters of men, and
communicates instruction without seeming to
assume the authority of a master or a pedagogue.
Æsop's situation as a slave might suggest this
method to him; for what would have been scorn-
fully rejected if delivered in an authoritative style
by a slave, was received with avidity in the form
of a fable.

Æsop had several masters; his second master
was Xanthus, in whose service he discovered
great wisdom and sagacity in answering ques-
tions, and reconciling differences. By the follow-
ing stratagem he made his master's wife return
back, after she had run away and left him, and
effectually reconciled them: our Fabulist, then a
slave, went to the market, and bought a great
quantity of the best provisions, which he pub-
licly declared were intended for the marriage of
his master with a new spouse. This report had
its desired effect, and the matter was amicably
composed. The story of his feast of *Neat Tongrege*,
and his answer to a gardener, are scarcely worthy

of relating. At a feast made on purpose to celebrate the return of his master's wife, he is said to have served the guests with several courses of tongues, by which he intended to give a moral lesson to his master and mistress, who had by the too liberal use of their tongues occasioned the difference which was now agreed.

The third master of Æsop was Idmon, who was surnamed the wise. Idmon was an inhabitant of the island of Samos. During Æsop's servitude with this master, he had a fellow-servant called Rhodopis, who some affirm was his wife. This does not at all appear credible, for there is no mention made of this among the Greek writers. This Rhodopis became afterwards very famous for her riches, and was celebrated all over Greece. Idmon is said to have been so well pleased with Æsop, that after he had been some time in his service, he emancipated him, and made him free. With the enjoyment of liberty, he acquired new reputation, and became celebrated for his wisdom. He is by some compared to the Seven Sages of Greece, and accounted their equal in wisdom. He had the honour to be acquainted with Solon and Chilo, and was equally admitted with them in the Court of Periander, the King of the Corinthians, who was himself one of the

Sages of Greece. He was much esteemed by
Crœsus, King of Lydia, and received into his
Court at Sardis. During his residence at Sardis,
he gave proofs of his sagacity which astonished
the courtiers of Crœsus. This ambitious Prince
having one day shown his wise men his vast
riches and magnificence, and the glory and splen-
dour of his court, asked them the question,
whom they thought the happiest man. After
several different answers given by all the wise
men present, it came at last to Æsop to make his
reply, who said: *That Crœsus was as much happier
than other men as the fulness of the sea was superior
to the rivers*. Whether this was spoken ironically
or in earnest does not appear so evident; but according to the severe morality of Æsop, it would
rather appear to be a sarcasm, though it was
otherwise understood by the King, and received
as the greatest compliment. It wrought so much
upon his vanity, that he exclaimed: *The Phrygian
had hit the mark*. One thing which renders it
probable that Æsop flattered Crœsus on this occasion is his conversation with Solon, who at
this time departed from the Court of the King of
Lydia. When they were upon the road, Æsop
exclaims: *O Solon! either we must not speak to Kings,
or we must say what will please them*. Solon replied:

We should either not speak to Kings at all, or we should give them good advice, and speak truth. This seems to be one instance in which Æsop is charged with flattery and dissimulation. Some writers praise him for his complaisance to so great a Prince; but it is rather a proof of his policy than his ordinary strictness and integrity. There is another instance recorded by some writers of the life of Æsop, of his complaisance to Princes, even contrary to the liberties of the people. He is said to have written a Fable in favour of the tyrant Pisistratus, which Phædrus has translated, and proves that he was reconciled to tyranny. But this is no way evident. There are many Fables which are mingled with those of Æsop, which are not his, yet have been fathered upon him; and it is not consistent with the other parts of his character and writings to suppose that he would either flatter tyrants or defend them. The authorities from whence these supposed facts are taken are not to be depended upon.

In all other particulars he appears to have proceeded upon the principles of wisdom, as far as any of the Sages of Greece. When he was asked by Chilo, one of the wise men, *What God was doing?* He replied, with great adroitness, *That he was humbling the proud and exalting the humble.* He had just views of human nature, and assigned true reasons for all its Phænomena. In an account of the paintings in the time of the Antonines, Philostratus informs us, that there is one of Æsop which makes a principal figure. The painter represents him before his own house, with the geniuses approaching him with a sort of adulating pleasure as the inventor of Fables: they are painted as adorning him with wreaths and chaplets of flowers, and crowning him with olive branches. His countenance appears in a smiling attitude, while his eyes seem fixed toward the ground, as if composing a Fable, with the same gaiety and good humour with which he usually wrote. There is a group of men and beasts placed around him, and amongst the rest the Fox, which makes a capital figure, as he does in the Fables. This picture does not represent Æsop in a decrepit form, but sets him forth with a mixture of gravity and good humour. The image of his mind is well drawn by Plutarch in his *Feast of the Sages at the Court of Periander*, who himself was one of the Seven. It was at this feast that Æsop repeats his Fable of *The Wolf and the Shepherds*, to show that the company were guilty of the same fault. From Plutarch's account it is manifest that Æsop's conversation was pleasant and witty, but yet deli-

cate. He was satirical without disobliging, and
the poignancy of his wit was smoothed with
good nature and good sense.

The writer of his life prefixed to Dodsley's
Fables compares him to Dean Swift, but with
very little propriety; for he has a delicacy in all
his wit which the Dean of St. Patrick's was a
total stranger to; and, what is more strange, he
had nearly as much Christianity.

It has been doubted if he was the inventor of
Fables; but it is certain he was the first that
brought that species of writing into reputation.
Archilochus is said to have written Fables one
hundred years before him; but it would appear
that those stories were not written for posterity
like those of Æsop. The Fables of Æsop were
written in prose, though the images that are in
them afford good scope for a poet, of which
Phrædus has given an elegant specimen. Æsop
writes with great simplicity, elegance, and neat-
ness; the schemes of his Fables are natural, the
sentiments just, and the conclusions moral. Quin-
tilian recommends his Fables as a first book for
children; and, when Plato had sent all the poets
into exile, he allows Æsop a residence in his
commonwealth. The Athenians were good judges
of literary merit, and erected a noble statue for

Æsop, to perpetuate his memory, which was sculped by the famous Lysippus.

The great excellency of Æsop's manner of writing is, that he blends the pleasing and the instructive so well as to instruct and please at once. Horace is much indebted to him for a plan of writing, and has formed a rule from this famous Fabulist:

> Omne tulit punctum, qui miscuit utile dulci;
> Lectorem delectando, pariterque monendo.
> —*De Arte Poet*. ver. 343.

I wish I could conceal the exit of this great Fabulist and Moral Writer. He was accused by the Delphians of sacrilege, and convicted by an act of the greatest villany that ever was invented. They concealed among his baggage, at his departure, some golden vessels consecrated to Apollo, and then despatched messengers to search his baggage. Upon this he was accused of theft and sacrilege, condemned, and precipitated over a rock. Thus ended the famous Æsop, whose Fables have immortalised his memory, and will hand down his name to the latest posterity.

Treasury of Aesop's Fables
with 68 *Engravings* by
Thomas Bewick
[1753-1828]

Fable 1

The Cock and the Jewel

To fools, the treasures dug from wisdom's mine
Are Jewels thrown to Cocks, and Pearls to Swine.

A BRISK young Cock, in company with two
or three pullets, his mistresses, raking upon
a Dunghill for something to entertain them with,
happened to scratch up a jewel. He knew what it
was well enough, for it sparkled with an exceeding bright lustre; but, not knowing what to do
with it, endeavoured to cover his ignorance under
a gay contempt. So, shrugging up his wings,
shaking his head, and putting on a grimace, he

expressed himself to this purpose: Indeed you are a very fine thing; but I know not any business you have here. I make no scruple of declaring that my taste lies quite another way; and I had rather have one grain of dear, delicious barley, than all the jewels under the sun.

Several very pretty fellows, who are as great strangers to the true uses of virtue and knowledge as the Cock upon the Dunghill is to the real value of the Jewel, endeavour to palliate their ignorance by pretending that their taste lies another way.

FABLE II

The City Mouse and Country Mouse

Heav'n in one mould the kindred fate has cast
Of men of dignity and mice of taste;
Traps, dangers, terrors are alike their lot:
Scar'd if they 'scape, and worry'd if they're caught.

A COUNTRY Mouse invited a City Sister of
hers to a collation, where she spared for
nothing that the place afforded—as mouldy crusts,
cheese-parings, musty oatmeal, rusty bacon, and
the like. The City Dame was too well bred to find
fault with her entertainment; but yet represented
that such a life was unworthy of a merit like

hers; and letting her know how splendidly she lived, invited her to accompany her to town. The Country Mouse consented, and away they trudged together, and about midnight got to their journey's end. The City Mouse shewed her friend the larder, the pantry, the kitchen, and other offices where she laid her stores; and after this, carried her into the parlour, where they found, yet upon the table, the relics of a mighty entertainment of that very night. The City Mouse carved her companion of what she liked best, and so to it they fell upon a velvet couch. The Country Mouse, who had never seen or heard of such doings before, blessed herself at the change of her condition—when, as ill luck would have it, all on a sudden the doors flew open, and in comes a crew of noisy servants of both sexes, to feast upon the dainties that were left. This put the poor mice to their wits' end how to save their skins—the stranger especially, who had never been in such danger before. But she made a shift, however, for the present to slink into a corner, where she lay trembling and panting till the company went away. As soon as ever the house was quiet again: Well, my Court Sister, says she, if this be the sauce to your rich meats, I'll e'en back to my cottage and my mouldy cheese again;

for I had much rather lie nibbling of crusts, without fear or hazard, in my own hole, than be mistress of all the delicacies in the world, and subject to such terrifying alarms and dangers.

This fable shews the difference between a Court and a Country Life: The delights, innocence, and security of the one, compared with the anxiety, voluptuousness, and hazards of the other.

FABLE III

The Fox and the Crow

"It is a maxim in the schools,
That Flattery's the food of fools:"
And whoso likes such airy meat
Will soon have nothing else to eat.

A CROW having taken a piece of cheese out of a cottage window, flew up into a high tree with it, in order to eat it. Which a Fox observing, came and sat underneath, and began to compliment the Crow upon the subject of her beauty. I protest, says he, I never observed it before, but your feathers are of a more delicate

white than any that ever I saw in my life! Ah!
what a fine shape and graceful turn of body is
there! And I make no question but you have a
tolerable voice. If it is but as fine as your complexion, I do not know a bird that can pretend
to stand in competition with you. The Crow,
tickled with this very civil language, nestled and
wriggled about, and hardly knew where she was;
but thinking the Fox a little dubious as to the
particular of her voice, and having a mind to set
him right in that matter, began to sing, and, in
the same instant, let the cheese drop out of her
mouth;—which the Fox presently chopt up, and
then bade her remember that whatever he had
said of her beauty, he had spoken nothing yet
of her brains.

*There is hardly any man living that may not be wrought
upon more or less by flattery; for we do all of us
naturally overween in our own favour. But when
it comes to be applied once to a vain fool, there is
no end then can be proposed to be attained by it,
but may be effected.*

Fable IV

𝔄n 𝔄ss, an 𝔄pe, and a 𝔐ole

The miseries of half mankind unknown,
Fools vainly think no sorrows like their own:
But view the world, and you will learn to bear
Misfortunes well, since all men have their share.

AN Ass and an Ape were conferring on griev-
ances. The Ass complained mightily for want
of horns, and the Ape was as much troubled for
want of a tail. Hold your tongues, both of ye,
says the Mole, and be thankful for what you
have; for the poor blind Moles are in a worse
condition than either of ye.

Fable v

The Hares and the Frogs

ONCE upon a time the Hares found themselves mightily unsatisfied with the miserable condition they lived in. Here we live, says one of them, at the mercy of men, dogs, eagles, and I know not how many other creatures, which prey upon us at pleasure; perpetually in frights, perpetually in danger; and therefore I am absolutely of opinion, that we had better die once for all, than live at this rate in a continual dread that's worse than death itself. The motion was seconded and debated, and a resolution immediately taken, by one and all, to drown themselves. The vote was no sooner passed, but away they scudded with that determination to the next lake. Upon this hurry there leapt a whole shoal of Frogs from the bank into the water, for fear of the Hares. Nay then, my masters, says one of the gravest of the company, pray let's have a little patience. Our condition, I find, is not altogether so bad as we fancied it; for there are those, you see, that are as much afraid of us as we are of others.

There is no contending with the Orders and Decrees of Providence. He that makes us, knows what is fittest for us; and every man's own lot (well understood and managed) is undoubtedly the best.

FABLE VI

𝔄𝔫 𝔄𝔫𝔱 𝔞𝔫𝔡 𝔉𝔩𝔶

Pert coxcombs, pleas'd with buzzing round the fair,
Laugh at the low mechanic's thrifty care;
While he with juster scorn may well deride
Their folly, meanness, indolence, and pride.

WHERE's the honour or the pleasure in the world, says the Fly, in a dispute for pre-eminence with the Ant, that I have not my part in? Are not all temples and places open to me? Am not I the taster to gods and princes in all their sacrifices and entertainments? And all this without either money or pains? I trample upon crowns, and kiss what ladies' lips I please. And what have you now to pretend to all this while? Vain boaster! says the Ant, dost thou not know the difference between the access of a *guest*, and that of an *intruder*? for people are so far from liking your company, that they kill you as soon as they catch you. You are a plague to them wherever you come. Your very breath has maggots in it; and for the kiss you brag of, what is it but the perfume of the last dunghill you touched upon, once removed? For my part, I live upon what's my own, and work honestly in the summer to maintain myself in the winter; whereas the whole course of your scandalous life is only cheating or sharping one half of the year, and starving the other.

The happiness of life does not lie so much in enjoying small advantages, as in living free from great inconveniences. An honest mediocrity is the happiest state a man can wish for.

FABLE VII

A Horse and an Ass

Proud of the clothes with which you are equipt,
You of your pride may easily be stript.

A PROUD pampered Horse, bedecked with
gaudy trappings, met in his course a poor
creeping Ass, under a heavy burden, that had
chopt into the same track with him. Why, how
now, sirrah, says he, do you not see by these
arms and trappings to what master I belong? and
do you not understand, that when I have that
master of mine upon my back, the whole weight
of the state rests upon my shoulders? Out of the

way, thou slavish insolent animal, or I'll tread
thee to dirt. The wretched Ass immediately slunk
aside, with this envious reflection between his
teeth, *What would I give to change conditions with
that happy creature there!* This fancy would not out
of the head of him, till it was his hap, a little
while after, to see this very Horse doing drudgery
in a common dung-cart. Why, how now, friend,
says the Ass, how comes this about? Only the
chance of war, says the other: I was a General's
horse, you must know; and my master carried me
into a battle, where I was hacked and maimed;
and you have here before your eyes the catas-
trophe of my fortune.

*This Fable shews the folly and the fate of pride and
arrogance; and the mistake of placing happiness
in anything that may be taken away; as also the
blessing of freedom in a mean estate.*

FABLE VIII

𝔄n 𝔥usbandman and 𝔖tork

The youth to temperance in vain pretends,
Who goes to taverns, and makes rakes his friends:
As maidens, who would live without a stain,
Should never choose to lodge in Drury-Lane.

A POOR innocent Stork had the ill hap to be
taken in a net that was laid for geese and
cranes. The Stork's plea for herself was simplicity
and piety, the love she bore to mankind, her duty
to her parents, and the service she did in picking
up venomous creatures. This may be all true, says
the Husbandman, for what I know; but as you

have been taken with ill company, you must expect to suffer with it.

Our fortune and reputation require us to keep good com-
  pany; for as we may be easily perverted by the force
  of bad examples, wise men will judge of us by the
  company we keep. What says the proverb? Birds
  of a feather will flock together.

FABLE IX

The Dog and the Shadow

Base is the man who pines amidst his store,
And fat with plenty, griping, covets more:
But doubly vile, by av'rice when betray'd,
He quits the substance for an empty shade.

A DOG, crossing a little rivulet with a piece of flesh in his mouth, saw his own shadow represented in the clear mirror of the limpid stream; and believing it to be another Dog who was carrying another piece of flesh, he could not forbear catching at it; but was so far from getting anything by his greedy design, that he dropt the

piece he had in his mouth, which immediately
sunk to the bottom, and was irrecoverably lost.

*Excessive greediness mostly in the end misses what it
aims at; disorderly appetites seldom obtain what
they would have; passions mislead men, and often
bring them into great straits and inconveniences,
through heedlessness and negligence.*

FABLE x

A Peacock and a Crane

Worth makes the man, and want of it the fellow,
The rest is all but leather or prunella.

AS a Peacock and a Crane were in company
together, the Peacock spread his tail, and
challenged the other to shew him such a fan of
feathers. You brag of your plumes, says the Crane,
that are fair indeed to the eye, but fit for nothing
but to attract the eyes of children and fools. Do
as I do, if you can; and then, with a suitable
contempt, he springs up into the air, leaving the

gaping Peacock staring after him till his eyes
ached.

*There cannot be a greater sign of a weak mind than
    a person's valuing himself on a gaudy outside;
    whether it be on the beauties of person, or the still
    vainer pride of fine clothes.*

FABLE XI

𝔄 𝔅𝔬𝔶 𝔞𝔫𝔡 𝔉𝔞𝔩𝔰𝔢 𝔄𝔩𝔞𝔯𝔪𝔰

Rank lies repeated oft, and oft detected,
Makes truth itself for a rank lie suspected.

A SHEPHERD's Boy kept his sheep upon a
common, and in sport and wantonness had
gotten a roguish trick of crying, A wolf! a wolf!
when there was no such matter, and fooling the
country people with false alarms. He had been at
this sport so many times in jest, that they would
not believe him at last when he was in earnest;

and so the wolves broke in upon the flock, and worried the sheep without resistance.

This fable shews us the dangerous consequences of an improper and unseasonable fooling. The old moral observes, that a common liar shall not be believed, even when he speaks true.

FABLE XII

𝕬 𝕱𝖆𝖙𝖍𝖊𝖗 𝖆𝖓𝖉 𝕳𝖎𝖘 𝕾𝖔𝖓𝖘

Distress and ruin on divisions wait,
But union is the bond of ev'ry state;
Disloyalty's a plague, dissension's worse,
And parties, where they rage, a kingdom's curse.

A VERY honest man happened to have a contentious brood of children. He called for a rod, and bade them try one after another, with all their force, if they could break it. They tried, and could not. Well, says he, unbind it now, and take every twig of it apart, and see what you can do that way. They did so, and with great ease, by one and one, they snapped it all to pieces. This, says he, is the true emblem of your condition: keep together, and you are safe; divide, and you are undone.

The breach of unity puts the world into a state of war, and turns every man's hand against his brother; but so long as that band holds, it is the strength of all the several parts of it gathered into one, and is not easily subdued.

FABLE XIII

The Sick Father and His Children

Assiduous pains the swelling coffers fill,
And all may make their fortune, if they will.

A COUNTRYMAN who had lived hand-somely in the world upon his honest labour and industry, was desirous his Sons should do so after him; and being now upon his death-bed, My dear children, says he, I reckon myself bound to tell you before I depart, that there is a considerable treasure hid in my vineyard; wherefore pray be sure to dig, and search narrowly for it, when I am gone. The Father dies, and the Sons fall immediately to work upon the vineyard. They turned it up over and over, and not one penny of money to be found there; but the profit of the next vintage expounded the riddle.

Good counsel is the best legacy a Father can leave to a Child; and it is still the better, when it is so wrapt up, as to beget a curiosity as well as an inclination to follow it.

FABLE XIV

𝕿𝖍𝖊 𝕾𝖙𝖆𝖌 𝖑𝖔𝖔𝖐𝖎𝖓𝖌 𝖎𝖓𝖙𝖔 𝖙𝖍𝖊 𝖂𝖆𝖙𝖊𝖗

Virtue despised, the beauty views her face,
And pleased beholds an angel in her glass;
But lost at length, to shame and want resigned,
Mourns she ne'er sought the beauty of the mind.

A STAG that had been drinking at a clear spring, saw himself in the water; and, pleased with the prospect, stood afterwards for some time contemplating and surveying his shape and features, from head to foot. Ah! says he, what a glorious pair of branching horns are there!

how gracefully do those antlers hang over my forehead, and give an agreeable turn to my whole face! If some other parts of my body were but proportionable to them, I would turn my back to nobody; but I have a set of such legs as really makes me ashamed to see them. People may talk what they please of their conveniences, and what great need we stand in of them upon several occasions; but for my part, I find them so very slender and unsightly, that I had as lief have none at all. While he was giving himself these airs, he was alarmed with the noise of some Huntsmen and a pack of hounds that had been just laid on upon the scent, and were making towards him. Away he flies in some consternation, and, bounding nimbly over the plain, threw dogs and men at a vast distance behind him. After which, taking a very thick copse, he had the ill-fortune to be entangled by his horns in a thicket; where he was held fast, till the hounds came in and pulled him down. Finding now how it was like to go with him, in the pangs of death, he is said to have uttered these words: Unhappy creature that I am! I am too late convinced, that what I prided myself in has been the cause of my undoing; and what I so much disliked, was the only thing that could have saved me.

*We should examine things deliberately, and candidly
consider their real usefulness before we place our
esteem on them; otherwise, like the foolish Stag,
we may happen to admire those accomplishments
which are of no real use, and often prove prejudicial
to us, while we despise those things on which our
safety may depend.*

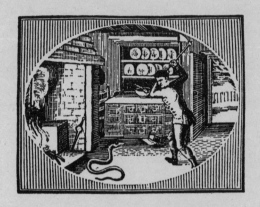

FABLE XV

The Countryman and the Snake

Evil for good, relentless to bestow,
Is all the gratitude th' unworthy know;
Mercy to such should be with caution shown;
Saving a villain's life, you risk your own.

A VILLAGER, in a frosty, snowy winter, found a Snake under a hedge, almost dead with cold. He could not help having compassion for the poor creature, so brought it home, and laid it upon the hearth near the fire; but it had not lain there long before (being revived with the heat) it began to erect itself, and fly at his wife and children, filling the whole cottage with dreadful hissings. The countryman hearing an outcry, and perceiving what the matter was, catched up a mattock, and soon dispatched him, upbraiding him at the same time in these words: "Is this, vile wretch, the reward you make to him that saved your life? Die, as you deserve; but a single death is too good for you."

It is no strange thing to see a reprobate fool throw his poisonous language about against those who are so inadvertent as to concern themselves with him.

FABLE XVI

A Gnat and a Bee

The wretch who works not for his daily bread,
Sighs and complains, but ought not to be fed.
Think, when you see stout beggars on their stand,
The lazy are the locusts of the land.

A GNAT, half starved with cold and hunger, went one frosty morning to a Bee-hive, to beg a charity; and offered to teach music in the Bee's family, for her diet and lodging. The Bee very civilly desired to be excused: For, says she, I bring up all my children to my own trade, that they may be able to get their living by their

industry; and I am sure I am right; for see what
that music, which you would teach my children,
has brought you yourself to.

*Industry ought to be diligently inculcated in the minds
of children of all ranks and degrees; for who stands
so sure as to say he is exempt from the vicissitudes
of this uncertain life?*

FABLE XVII

𝔐𝔢𝔯𝔠𝔲𝔯𝔶 𝔞𝔫𝔡 𝔱𝔥𝔢 𝔚𝔬𝔬𝔡𝔪𝔞𝔫

Truth, sacred truth, shall flourish and prevail,
While all the arts of fraud and falsehood fail;
The flimsy cheat wise judges soon descry;
Sure those will rob, *who scruple not to* lie.

A MAN was felling a tree on the bank of a
river; and by chance let his hatchet slip out
of his hand, which dropt into the water, and
immediately sunk to the bottom. Being therefore
in great distress for the loss of his tool, he sat
down and bemoaned himself most lamentably.
Upon this, *Mercury* appeared to him, and, being

informed of the cause of his complaint, dived to the bottom of the river, and coming up again, showed the man a golden hatchet, demanding if that were his. He denied that it was. Upon which *Mercury* dived a second time, and brought up a silver one. The man refused it, alleging likewise that this was not his. He dived a third time, and fetched up the individual hatchet the man had lost; upon sight of which the poor wretch was overjoyed, and took it with all humility and thankfulness. *Mercury* was so pleased with the fellow's honesty, that he gave him the other two into the bargain, as a reward for his just dealing. The man goes to his companions, and giving them an account of what had happened, one of them went presently to the river's side, and let his hatchet fall designedly into the stream. Then sitting down upon the bank, he fell a weeping and lamenting, as if he had been really and sorely afflicted. *Mercury* appeared as before, and diving, brought up a golden hatchet, asking if that was the hatchet he lost. Transported at the precious metal, he answered, Yes; and went to snatch it greedily. But the god detesting his abominable impudence, not only refused to give him that, but would not so much as let him have his own hatchet again.

*Honesty is the best policy; religion absolutely requires
it of its votaries: and the honest man, provided
his other talents are not deficient, always carries
the preference in our esteem, before any other, in
whatever business he employs himself.*

FABLE XVIII

𝕿𝖍𝖊 𝕱𝖎𝖗 𝖆𝖓𝖉 𝖆 𝕭𝖗𝖆𝖒𝖇𝖑𝖊

Minions of fortune, pillars of the state,
 Round your exalted heads what tempests low'r!
While peace secure, and soft contentment wait
 On the calm mansions of the humble poor.

MY head, says the boasting Fir-tree to the humble Bramble, is advanced among the stars; I furnish beams for palaces, and masts for shipping; the very sweat of my body is a sovereign remedy for the sick and wounded: whereas thou, O rascally Bramble, runnest creeping in the dirt, and art good for nothing in the world but mis-

chief. I pretend not to vie with thee, said the
Bramble, in the points thou gloriest in. But, not
to insist upon it, that He who made thee a lofty
Fir, could have made thee an humble Bramble,
I pray thee tell me, when the Carpenter comes
next with the axe into the wood, to fell timber,
whether thou hadst not rather be a Bramble than
a Fir-tree?

*Poverty secures a man from many dangers; whereas the
rich and the mighty are the mark of malice and
cross fortune; and still the higher they are, the
nearer the thunder.*

FABLE XIX

The Fox and the Countryman

Thus by the knave, in worldly guile adept,
Vows are perform'd and promises are kept:
True to the form, and fearful of offence,
Good soul! he swerves from nothing but the sense.

A FOX being hard hunted, and having run a long chase, was quite tired. At last he spied a country fellow in a wood, to whom he applied for refuge, entreating that he would give him leave to hide himself in his cottage, till the hounds were gone by. The man consented, and the Fox went and covered himself up close in a

corner of the hovel. Presently the hunters came
up, and inquired of the man, if he had seen the
Fox. No, says he, I have not seen him indeed:
but all the while he pointed with his finger to
the place where the Fox was hid. However, the
hunters did not understand him, but called off
their hounds, and went another way. Soon after,
the Fox, creeping out of his hole, was going to
sneak off; when the man, calling after him, asked
him, if that was his manners, to go away without thanking his benefactor, to whose fidelity he
owed his life. *Reynard*, who had peeped all the
while, and seen what passed, answered, I know
what obligations I have to you well enough; and
I assure you, if your actions had but been agreeable to your words, I should have endeavoured,
however incapable of it, to have returned you
suitable thanks.

*To appear in another's interest, while underhand we are
    giving intelligence to their enemies, is treacherous,
    knavish, and base.*

FABLE XX

A One-Eyed Stag

The man whom we fear and suspect for a cheat,
Can hardly delude us with art and deceit;
But he, in whose faith we securely confide,
May come round with impunity on our blind side.

A ONE-EYED Stag that was afraid of the
Huntsmen at land, kept a watch that way,
and fed with his blind side towards an arm of
the sea, where he thought there was no danger.
In this hope of security, he was shot, by a ball
from a boat, and so ended his days with this
lamentation: Here I am destroyed, says he, where

I reckoned myself to be safe on the one hand; and no evil has befallen me, where I most dreaded it, on the other. But it is my comfort that I intended the best.

We are liable to many accidents that no care or foresight can prevent: but we are to provide, however, the best we can against them, and leave the rest to Providence.

FABLE XXI

𝕬 𝖘𝖍𝖊𝖕𝖍𝖊𝖗𝖉 𝖆𝖓𝖉 𝖆 𝖄𝖔𝖚𝖓𝖌 𝖂𝖔𝖑𝖋

The knave profest may seem a gen'rous foe,
Deserves a rope, yet claims our pity too;
But dragg'd to light, and stript of his disguise,
The sneaking hypocrite unpitied dies.

A SHEPHERD took a Wolf's sucking Whelp,
and trained it up with his Dogs. The Whelp
fed with them, grew up with them, and when-
soever they went out upon the chase of a Wolf,
the Whelp would be sure to make one. It fell
out sometimes that the Wolf escaped; but this
domestic Wolf would be still hunting on, after

the dogs had given over the chase, till he came
up to his true brethren, where he took part of the
prey with them, and then went back again to his
master. And when he could come in for no snacks
with the Wolves, he would now and then make
free, by the by, with a straggling Sheep out of
the flock. He carried on this trade for a while;
but at last he was caught in the fact, and hanged
by his injured master.

*Men naturally false and treacherous are no more to be
reclaimed than Wolves. Benefits but augment their
power to do mischief, and they never fail to make
use of it to the prejudice of their benefactors.*

FABLE XXII

Seamen Praying to Saints

Inactive wishes are but waste of time,
And, without efforts, pray'rs themselves a crime:
Vain are their hopes, who miracles expect,
And ask from heaven what themselves neglect.

IN a terrible tempest at Sea, one Seaman took notice that the rest of his fellows were praying severally to so many Saints. Have a care, my masters, says he, what you do; for what if we should all be drowned now before the messenger can deliver his errand? would it not be better, without going so far about, to pray to Him that can save us without help.

A wise man will take the nearest and surest way to obtain his end, and to commit no business of importance to a proxy, where he may do it himself.

FABLE XXIII

A Fox that had lost his Tail

Gladly Sir Clumsy *would the world persuade,*
Not he, but all mankind are vilely made;
And might the purblind and the deaf advise,
'Twere better for to want both ear and eyes.

A FOX taken in a trap was glad to compound for his neck, by leaving his tail behind him. It was so uncouth a sight for a Fox to appear without a tail, that the very thought of it made him weary of his life: but, however, for the better countenance of the scandal, he got the *Master and Wardens of the Foxes' company* to call a *Court of*

Assistants, where he himself appeared, and made
a learned discourse upon the trouble, the useless-
ness, and the indecency of Foxes wearing tails.
He had no sooner said out his say, but up rises a
cunning Snap, then at the board, who desired to
be informed, whether the worthy member that
moved against the wearing of tails, gave his
advice for the advantage of those that *had tails*,
or to palliate the deformity and disgrace of those
that *had none*.

*It is the way of the world to give other people counsel for
by-ends. But yet it is a hard matter to over-rule a
multitude to their own pain and loss.*

FABLE XXIV

A Scoffer Punished

That there's a God all nature loud proclaims,
Tho' the vile Atheist the great truth disclaims;
Or warp'd by prejudice, or sunk in sin,
His fright'ned conscience feels the lash within.

A PRESUMPTUOUS Scoffer at things sacred
took a journey to *Delphi*, on purpose to try
if he could put a trick upon *Apollo*. He carried a
sparrow in his hand under his coat, and told the
god, *I have something in my hand*, says he: *Is it dead
or living*? If the oracle should say it was dead, he
could show it alive; if living, it was but squeezing

it, and then it was dead. He that saw the iniquity of his heart, gave him this answer: It shall e'en be which of the two thou pleasest: for it is in thy choice to have it either the one or the other, as to the bird, but it is not in thy power as to thyself; and immediately struck the bold scoffer dead, for a warning to others.

Presumption naturally leads people to infidelity, and that by insensible degrees to atheism: for when men have once cast off a reverence for religion, they are come within one step of laughing at it.

FABLE XXV

A Swan and a Stork

This life's a scene of bustle, care, and noise,
Of certain trouble, and uncertain joys,
Death ends the contest, we can only have
A peaceful refuge in the silent grave.

A STORK that was present at the song of a dying Swan, told her, it was contrary to nature to sing so much out of season; and asked her the reason of it. Why, says the Swan, I am now entering into a state where I shall be no longer in danger of either snares, guns, or hunger; and who would not joy at such a deliverance?

Death is a certain relief from all the difficulties, pains, and hazards of life.

FABLE XXVI

𝕬 𝖘𝖜𝖆𝖑𝖑𝖔𝖜 𝖆𝖓𝖉 𝖆 𝖘𝖕𝖎𝖉𝖊𝖗

They who by imitations covet fame,
Oft incur dangers, and solicit shame;
For though the bright original we prize,
His abject imitator all despise.

A SPIDER that observed a Swallow catching of flies, fell immediately to work upon a net to catch Swallows; for she looked upon it as an encroachment upon her right: but the birds, without any difficulty, brake through the work, and flew away with the very net itself. Well, says the Spider, bird-catching is none of my talent,

I perceive; and so she returned to her old trade of catching flies again.

A wise man will not undertake anything without means answerable to the end.

FABLE XXVII

𝔄 𝔇𝔬𝔤, 𝔞 ℭ𝔬𝔠𝔨, 𝔞𝔫𝔡 𝔞 𝔉𝔬𝔵

Happy the ready wit of men of parts,
Who on himself can turn the villain's arts!

A DOG and a Cock took a journey together. The Dog kennelled in the body of a hollow tree, and the Cock roosted at night upon the boughs. The Cock crowed about midnight (at his usual hour), which brought a Fox that was abroad upon the hunt immediately to the tree; and there he stood licking of his lips at the Cock, and, wheedling him to get him down, he protested he never heard so angelical a voice since he was born; and what would not he do now, to hug the creature that had given him so admirable a serenade? Pray, says the Cock, speak to the porter below to open the door, and I'll come down to you. The Fox, little dreaming of the Dog so near, did as he was directed, and the Dog presently seized and worried him.

When a man has to do with an adversary who is too crafty or too strong for him, it is right to turn him off to his match.

FABLE XXVIII

The Ants and a Grasshopper

O now, while health and vigour still remain,
Toil, toil, my lads, to purchase honest gain!
Shun idleness! shun pleasure's tempting snare!
A youth of revels breeds an age of care.

AS the Ants were airing their provisions one
winter, a hungry Grasshopper begged a
charity of them. They told him, that he should
have wrought in summer, if he would not have
wanted in winter. Well, says the Grasshopper,
but I was not idle neither; for I sung out the
whole season. Nay then, said they, you'll e'en

do well to make a merry year of it, and dance in winter to the tune that you sung in summer.

Action and industry is the business of a wise and a good man, and nothing is so much to be despised as slothfulness. Go to the Ant, thou sluggard, *says the Royal Preacher,* consider her ways, and be wise; *which in a few words sums up the moral of this fable.*

FABLE XXIX

𝕿𝖍𝖊 𝕭𝖆𝖑𝖉 𝕮𝖆𝖛𝖆𝖑𝖎𝖊𝖗

When the loud laugh prevails at your expense,
All want of temper is but want of sense;
Would you disarm the sneerer of his jest,
Frown not, but laugh in concert with the rest.

WHEN periwigs were first used, and then
chiefly to cover the defect of baldness, a
certain Cavalier had one for that purpose, which
passed for his own hair. But as he was one day
riding out with some others a hunting, a sudden
puff of wind blew off both his wig and his hat,
and set the company in a loud laugh at his bald

pate. He, for his part, fell a laughing with the
rest, and said, Why, really, Gentlemen, this is
merry enough; for how could I expect to keep
other people's hair, who could not preserve my
own.

The edge of a jest is quite blunted and turned off when
a man has presence of mind to join in it against
himself, or begin it.

FABLE XXX

A Dog and a Cat

NEVER were two creatures better together than a Dog and a Cat brought up in the same house from a Whelp and a Kitten; so kind, so gamesome and diverting, that it was half the entertainment of the family to see the gambols and love-tricks that passed betwixt them. Only it was observed, that still at meal-times, when scraps fell from the table, or a bone was thrown to them, they would be snarling and spitting at one another under the table like the worst of foes.

But as the sun, refulgent globe of light,
By mists obscur'd, may shine more dimly bright;
Or by some sable cloud its lustre veil'd,
Lie hid in darkness from the world conceal'd;
So every joy which mortals here can know
Is damp'd by sorrow, or is mix'd with woe.
Pleasure entire, from all assaults secure,
To no one's granted, no one can ensure.

    Ungovern'd passions to such heights will rise,
That friendship's self oft falls a sacrifice;
A fire is kindled in the human breast,
By words misconstru'd, or a simple jest,
As some one relish often spoils a feast.
Thus sportful, frisking on the sunny green,
Two lambkins loving are not seldom seen:
Off from the flock they to a distance stray,
And all a battle represent in play;
Till some unlucky thrusts rouse up their rage,
Pretence is gone, in earnest they engage.

    Those whom she sung, the muse reluctant sees
Differ for causes trivial as these;
And full of anguish, sighing and alone,
Pours out her deep-felt melancholy moan:——
"Where dwelt their mutual fondness in that hour
When love took leave, and kindness now no more?
Alas! no more, in social converse join'd,
Shall they partake the rapture of the mind?

Placid content, shall fell disgust succeed,
And vexing discord make enjoyment bleed?
Forbid it, Heav'n! and to them gracious deign
Their strict agreeing harmony again!
All jarring thoughts at utmost distance keep,
And bid the former in oblivion sleep!''

FABLE XXXI

An Impertinent and Philosopher

"Swift *is obscure, and* Addison *wants taste,*
Shakespeare *is low, and* Milton *all bombast*"
Thus wit itself half-seeing fools condemn,
And sense and genius are all dark to them.

A CERTAIN pragmatical, gay, fluttering Cox-
comb would needs make a visit to a Philosopher. He found him alone in his study, and fell
a wondering how he could endure to lead so
solitary a life. Sir, says the Philosopher, you are
exceedingly mistaken, for I was in very good
company till you came in.

*What the noisy and most numerous part of the world
calls good company, is generally the most irksome
and insipid thing in the world to a wise man; a
mere round of folly and impertinence, and void of
any kind of instruction or benefit to a reflecting
mind. How preferable to such a man must it be
to converse with the learned dead, rather than the
unedifying and noisy living?*

FABLE XXXII

𝕿𝖍𝖊 𝕱𝖔𝖝 𝖆𝖓𝖉 𝖙𝖍𝖊 𝕬𝖘𝖘

The fop, with empty jests and silly smile,
Women, or men like women, may beguile;
Howe'er with fools his senseless prate may pass,
The man of sense soon knows him for an Ass.

AN Ass, finding a Lion's skin, disguised himself
with it, and ranged about the forest, putting
all the beasts that saw him into a bodily fear.
After he had diverted himself thus for some time,
he met a Fox; and being desirous to fright him
too, as well as the rest, he leapt at him with some
fierceness, and endeavoured to imitate the roaring

of the Lion. Your humble servant, says the Fox; if you had held your tongue, I might have taken you for a Lion, as others did; but now you bray, I know who you are.

The more distant any person is from the thing he affects to appear, the stronger will the ridicule be which he excites, and the greater the inconveniencies into which he runs himself.

FABLE XXXIII

𝔄 𝔅oar and a 𝔉ox

Wise are the people, who in peace prepare
Their fleets and armies for the distant war;
Who ne'er in treaties and conventions trust,
Nor leave the sword, though it be sheath'd, to rust.

AS a Boar was whetting his teeth against a tree,
up comes a Fox to him. Pray, what do you
mean by that? says he. I do it, says the Boar, to
be in readiness in case of an attack by an enemy.
But, replies the Fox, I see no occasion for it, for
there is no enemy near you. Well, says the Boar,
but I see occasion for it; for when I come once

to be set upon, it will be too late for me to be whetting when I should be fighting.

A discreet man should have a reserve of everything that is necessary beforehand, that when the time comes for him to make use of them, he may not be in a hurry and confusion.

Fable xxxiv

𝕿𝖍𝖊 𝕯𝖎𝖘𝖈𝖔𝖓𝖙𝖊𝖓𝖙𝖊𝖉 𝕬𝖘𝖘

Who lacks the pleasures of a tranquil mind,
Will something wrong in every station find;
His mind unsteady, and on changes bent,
Is always shifting, yet is ne'er content.

AN Ass, in a hard winter, wished for a little warm weather, and a mouthful of fresh grass to nap upon, in exchange for a heartless truss of straw, and a cold lodging. In good time the warm weather and the fresh grass came on; but so much toil and business along with it, that the Ass grows quickly as sick of the spring as he was of the winter. He next longs for summer; and when that comes, finds his toils and drudgery greater than in the spring; and then he fancies he shall never be well till autumn comes: but there again, what with carrying apples, grapes, fuel, winter provisions, and such like, he finds himself in a greater hurry than ever. In fine, when he has trod the circle of the year in a course of restless labour, his last prayer is for winter again, and that he may but take up his rest where he began his complaint.

The life of an unsteady man runs away in a course of vain wishes, and unprofitable discontent; an unsettled mind can never be at rest. There is no season without its business.

FABLE XXXV

The Undutiful Young Lion

AMONG other good counsels that an old ex-
perienced Lion gave to his whelp, this was
one, that he should never contend with a man:
for, says he, if ever you do, you'll be worsted.
The little Lion gave his father the hearing, and
kept the advice in his thought, but it never went
near his heart. When he came to be grown up,
afterwards, and in the flower of his strength and
vigour, about he ranges to look for a man to
grapple with. In his ramble he met with a yoke
of oxen, and then with a horse, saddled and
bridled, and severally asked them if they were

men; but they saying they were not, he goes after this to one that was cleaving of blocks: D'ye hear? says the Lion, you seem to be a man: And a man I am, says the fellow. That's well, quoth the Lion, and dare you fight with me? Yes, says the man, I dare: why, I can tear all these blocks to pieces, you see. Put your feet now into this gap, where you see an iron thing there, and try what you can do. The Lion presently put his paws into the gaping of the wood, and with one lusty pluck made it give way, and out drops the wedge; the wood immediately closing upon it, there was the Lion caught by the toes. The Wood-man presently upon this raises the country, and the Lion finding what a strait he was in, gave one hearty twitch and got his feet out of the trap, but left his claws behind him. So away he goes back to his father, all lame and bloody, with this confession in his mouth: Alas! my dear father, says he, *this had never been, if I had followed your advice.*

The vengeance of Heaven, sooner or later, treads upon the heels of wilful disobedience to parents.

When wayward children in the pride of youth,
Scorn wisdom's precepts, and the curb of truth;

Laugh at experience, and her sagest rules,
And holds restraints the doting fits of fools;
They thoughtless rush, where folly leads the way,
Where evils throng, and vice holds lordly sway.
Yet hoary age by long experience knows,
Where vices flourish, and where evil grows;
With cautious fondness for the budding mind,
Warns from the path, where ill with ill's combin'd;
Whilst heedless youth, in all the pomp of pride,
Spurn at his prudence, and his laws deride.
A few short years disperse the dazzling shade,
Which fame excited, and which transports made;
Wearied and pall'd and pleasure's fleeting joys,
Which madness raves for, and which health destroys;
Too late they find, by sage experience taught,
The rules of age are with true wisdom fraught.

FABLE XXXVI

The Countryman and Ass

The man that is poor may be void of all care,
If there's nothing to hope, he has nothing to fear:
Whether stocks rise or fall, or whate'er be the news,
He is sure not to win, and has nothing to lose.

AN old fellow was feeding an Ass in a fine green meadow; and being alarmed with the sudden approach of the enemy, was impatient with the Ass to put himself forward, and fly with all the speed that he was able. The Ass asked him, Whether or no he thought the enemy would clap two pair of panniers upon his back?

The man said, No, there was no fear of that.
Why then, says the Ass, I will not stir an inch;
for what is it to me who my master is, since I
shall but carry my panniers as usual?

*Men in a fright, or alarmed with the apprehensions
of some imminent danger to themselves, often fly
for succour to those from whom they have not de-
served any. It is prudent so to behave in our prosperity, as that we may make every one our friend
in times of adversity: for no one is exempted from
the mutability of fortune.*

Fable xxxvii

Joy and Sorrow

JOY and Sorrow, two twin-sisters, once quarrelled vehemently who should have the preference; and being unable to decide the matter, left it to *Minos* to determine. He tried all means to make them agree and go hand in hand together, as loving sisters ought; but finding his counsel had no effect upon them, he decreed that they should be linked together in a chain; and each of them in turn should be perpetually treading upon the heel of the other; and not a pin matter then, says he, which goes foremost.

No man is to presume in prosperity, or despair in ad-
    versity; for good and ill fortune do as naturally
    succeed one another, as day and night.

The Gods one time, as poets feign,
Would pleasure intermix with pain;
And perfectly incorporate so,
As one from t' other none might know;
That mortals might alike partake
The Good and Evil which they make.

In mighty bowl they put these twain,
And stirr'd and stirr'd, but all in vain:
Pleasure would sometimes float aloft,
And pain keep pleasure down as oft:
Yet still from one another fly,
Detesting either's company.

The Gods, who saw they sooner might
Mix fire and water, day and night,
Unanimously they decreed
They should alternately succeed;
Each other's motions still pursue,
And a perpetual round renew:
Yet still divided should remain,
Tho' link'd together with a chain.

Thence comes it that we never see
A perfect bliss or misery;
Each happiness has some alloy;
And grief *succeeded is by* joy.
The happiest *mortal needs must own*
He has a time of sorrow *known:*
Nor can the poorest *wretch deny*
But it his life he felt a joy.

FABLE XXXVIII

The Fox and the Ape

When nations raise an idiot to the throne,
He shows the people's weakness and his own.

ONCE upon a time, the beasts were so void of reason as to choose an Ape for their King. He had danced, and diverted them with playing antic tricks, and truly nothing would serve but they must anoint him their sovereign. Accordingly crowned he was, and affected to look very wise and politic. But the Fox, vexed at his heart to see his fellow-brutes act so foolishly, was resolved the first opportunity to convince them of their sorry choice, and punish their jackanapes of a king for his presumption. Soon after, spying a trap in a ditch, which was baited with a piece of flesh, he went and informed the Ape of it, as a treasure, which, being found upon the waste, belonged to his Majesty only. The Ape, dreaming nothing of the matter, went very briskly to take possession, but had no sooner laid his paws upon the bait, than he was caught in the trap; where, betwixt shame and anger, he began to reproach the Fox, calling him rebel and traitor, and threatening to be revenged of him. At all which *Reynard* laughed heartily; and going off, added, with a sneer, You a king, and not understand trap!

When Apes are in power, Foxes will never be wanting to play upon them.

FABLE XXXIX

The Satyr and the Traveller

With such an inmate who would be perplext,
One hour all coldness, and all heat the next!
Who would his fev'rish shiv'ring fits endure?
That ague of the heart, no drug can cure.

A SATYR, as he was ranging the Forest in an
exceeding cold, snowy season, met with a
Traveller half-starved with the extremity of the
weather. He took compassion on him, and kind-
ly invited him home, to a warm comfortable
cave he had in the hollow of a rock. As soon as
they had entered and sat down, notwithstanding

there was a good fire in the place, the chilly
Traveller could not forbear blowing his finger
ends. Upon the Satyr's asking him why he did
so, he answered: That he did it to warm his
hands. The honest silvan having seen little of the
world, admired a man who was master of so
valuable a quality as that of blowing heat, and
therefore was resolved to entertain him in the
best manner he could. He spread the table before
him with dried fruits of several sorts; and produced a remnant of old cordial wine, which, as
the rigour of the season made very proper, he
mulled with some warm spices, infused over the
fire, and presented to his shivering guest. But
this the Traveller thought fit to blow likewise;
and upon the Satyr's demanding a reason why
he blowed again, he replied: To cool his dish.
This second answer provoked the Satyr's indignation, as much as the first had kindled his surprise. So, taking the man by the shoulder, he
thrust him out of doors, saying: He would have
nothing to do with a wretch who had so vile a
quality as to blow hot and cold with the same
mouth.

There is no conversing with any man that carries two
faces under one hood.

FABLE XL

𝕿𝖍𝖊 𝕰𝖆𝖌𝖑𝖊, 𝖙𝖍𝖊 𝕮𝖆𝖙, 𝖆𝖓𝖉 𝖙𝖍𝖊 𝕾𝖔𝖜

Ill fares that neighbourhood, where sland'rers meet
With easy faith to back their base deceit:
From house to house the plague of discord spreads,
And brings down ruin on their hapless heads.

AN Eagle had built her nest upon the top
branches of an old oak. A wild Cat in-
habited a hole in the middle; and in the hollow
part at the bottom was a Sow, with a whole
litter of pigs. A happy neighbourhood; and might
long have continued so, had it not been for the
wicked insinuations of the designing Cat. For,

first of all, up she crept to the Eagle; and, good
neighbour, says she, we shall be all undone: That
filthy Sow yonder does nothing but lie routing
at the foot of the tree, and, as I suspect, intends
to grub it up, that she may the more easily come
at our young ones. For my part I will take care
of my own concerns; you may do as you please,
but I will watch her motions, though I stay at
home this month for it. When she had said this,
which could not fail of putting the Eagle into
a great fright, down she went, and made a visit
to the Sow at the bottom; and, putting on a
sorrowful face, I hope, says she, you do not intend to go abroad to-day? Why not? says the
Sow. Nay, replies the other, you may do as you
please; but I overheard the Eagle tell her young
ones, that she would treat them with a pig the
first time she saw you go out; and I am not sure
but she may take up with a kitten in the mean-
time; so, good-morrow to you; you will excuse
me, I must go and take care of the little folks
at home. Away she went accordingly; and, by
contriving to steal out softly at nights for her
prey, and to stand watching and peeping all day
at her hole, as under great concern, she made such
an impression upon the Eagle and the Sow, that
neither of them dared to venture abroad for fear

of the other. The consequence of which was, that themselves, and their young ones, in a little time were all starved, and made prize of by the treacherous Cat and her kittens.

There can be no peace in any state or family where whisperers and tale-bearers are encouraged.

FABLE XLI

𝕿𝖍𝖊 𝕮𝖔𝖈𝖐 𝖆𝖓𝖉 𝖙𝖍𝖊 𝕱𝖔𝖝

Take courage, hence, ye wise, nor dread deceit;
Good sense and craft, how seldom do they meet!
Tho' keen, yet feeble, are the sharper's tools,
And cunning's the peculiar gift of fools.

A COCK being perched among the branches of a lofty Tree, crowed aloud, so that the shrillness of his voice echoed through the wood and invited a Fox to the place, who was prowling in that neighbourhood, in quest of his prey. But *Reynard*, finding the Cock was inaccessible, by reason of the height of his situation, had recourse to stratagem, in order to decoy him down; so, approaching the tree, Cousin, says he, I am heartily glad to see you; but at the same time I cannot forbear expressing my uneasiness at the inconvenience of the place, which will not let me pay my respects to you in a handsomer manner; though I suppose you will come down presently, and so that difficulty is easily removed. Indeed, Cousin, says the Cock, to tell you the truth I don't think it safe to venture myself upon the ground, for though I am convinced how much you are my friend, yet I may have the misfortune to fall into the clutches of some other beast, and what will become of me then? O dear, says *Reynard*, is it possible that you can be so ignorant, as not to know of the peace that has been lately proclaimed between all kinds of birds and beasts; and that we are, for the future, to forbear hostilities on all sides, and to live in the utmost love and harmony, and that under penalty of suffering the severest punishment that can be inflicted? All this while the Cock seemed to give little attention to what was said, but stretched out his neck, as if he saw something at a distance: Cousin, says the Fox, what's that you look at so earnestly? Why, says the Cock, I think I see a pack of hounds yonder a little way off.

Oh then, says the Fox, your humble servant, I must be gone. Nay, pray, Cousin, don't go, says the Cock, I'm just coming down; sure you are not afraid of dogs in these peaceable times. No, no, says he; but ten to one whether they have heard of the proclamation yet.

Perfidious people are naturally to be suspected in reports that favour their own interest.

FABLE XLII

Age to be Honoured

Though vig'rous health thy tide of life sustains,
And youthful manhood revels in thy veins:
With rev'rend awe regard the bending sage,
Nor thoughtless mock th' infirmities of age.

A PERT and inconsiderate young Man happened to meet an old Man, whose age and infirmity had brought his body almost to the shape of a bent bow. Pray, father, says he, will you sell your bow? Save your money, you fool, says the other; for when you come to my years, you shall have such a bow for nothing.

There cannot be a greater folly and impertinence, than
that of young men scoffing at the infirmities of age.

FABLE XLIII

𝕿𝔥𝔢 𝕾𝔭𝔩𝔢𝔫𝔢𝔱𝔦𝔠 𝕿𝔯𝔞𝔳𝔢𝔩𝔩𝔢𝔯

Who with vain fancies do themselves possess,
Are never bless'd, or can never bless;
Their life perplex'd, and fretful to no end—
The truly wise on Providence depend.

A SPLENETIC and a facetious man were once upon a journey: the former went slugging on with a thousand cares and troubles in his head, exclaiming over and over: "Lord, what shall I do to live?" The other jogged merrily away, and left his matters to Providence and good fortune. "Well, brother," says the sorrowful wight,

"how can you be so frolicksome now? As I am
a sinner, my heart's e'en ready to break for fear
I should want bread." "Come, come," says the
other, "fall back, fall edge, I have fixed my resolution, and my mind's at rest." "Ay, but for
all that," says the other, "I have known the
confidence of as resolute people as yourself has
deceived them in the conclusion;" and so the
poor man fell into another fit of doubting and
musing, till he started out of it all on a sudden:
"Good Sir!" says he, "what if I should fall
blind?" and so he walked a good way before
his companion with his eyes shut, to try how
it would be if that misfortune should befall him.
In this interim, his fellow-traveller, who followed him, found a purse of money upon the way,
which rewarded his trust in Providence; whereas
the other missed that encounter as a punishment
of his distrust; for the purse had been his, as he
went first, if he had not put himself out of condition of seeing it.

*He that commits himself to Providence is sure of a friend
in time of need; while an anxious distrust of the
divine goodness makes a man more and more unworthy of it, and miserable beforehand for fear of
being so afterwards.*

FABLE XLIV

𝕿𝖍𝖊 𝖄𝖔𝖚𝖓𝖌 𝕸𝖆𝖓 𝖆𝖓𝖉 𝖙𝖍𝖊 𝕾𝖜𝖆𝖑𝖑𝖔𝖜

Still blind to reason, nature, and his God,
Youth follows pleasure, till he feels the rod
Of sad experience, then bemoans his fate,
Nor sees his folly till it is too late.

A PRODIGAL young spendthrift, who had
wasted his whole patrimony in taverns and
gaming-houses among lewd, idle company, was
taking a melancholy walk near a brook. It was
in the month of *January*, and happened to be one
of those warm sunshiny days which sometimes

smile upon us even in that wintry season of the
year; and to make it the more flattering, a
swallow, which had made its appearance by
mistake too soon, flew skimming along upon the
surface of the water. The giddy youth, observing
this, without any further consideration, concluded that summer was now come, and that he
should have little or no occasion for clothes, so
went and pawned them at the broker's, and
ventured the money for one stake more, among
his sharping companions. When this too was
gone the same way with the rest, he took another
solitary walk in the same place as before. But
the weather, being severe and frosty, had made
everything look with an aspect very different
from what it did before: the brook was quite
frozen over, and the poor swallow lay dead upon
the bank of it; the very sight of which cooled
the young spark's brains, and coming to a kind
of sense of his misery, he reproached the deceased
bird as the author of all his misfortunes: Ah,
wretch that thou wert! says he, thou hast undone
both thyself and me, who was so credulous as
to depend upon thee.

*Some will listen to no conviction but what they derive
from fatal experience.*

FABLE XLV

The Brother and Sister

Ill manners may deform the fairest face,
But gentleness gives ugliness a grace:
Sure snarling Veny's *beauty less we prize,*
Than Pug's *black nose with his good-natured eyes.*

A CERTAIN man had two children, a son and a daughter: The boy beautiful and handsome enough; the girl not quite so well. They were both very young, and happened one day to be playing near the looking-glass, which stood on their mother's toilet. The boy, pleased with the novelty of the thing, viewed himself for

some time, and, in a wanton roguish manner,
took notice to the girl how handsome he was.
She resented it, and could not bear the insolent
manner in which he did it; for she understood
it (how could she do otherwise) as intended for a
direct affront to her. Therefore she ran immediately to her father, and, with a great deal of
aggravation, complained of her brother; partic-
ularly, for having acted so effeminate a part as
to look in a glass, and meddle with things which
belonged to women only. The father, embracing
them both with much tenderness and affection,
told them, that he should like to have them both
look in the glass every day; to the intent that
you, says he to the boy, if you think that face
of yours handsome, you may not disgrace and
spoil it by an ugly temper and a foul behaviour.
You, says he, speaking to the girl, that you may
make up for the defects of your person, if there
be any, by the sweetness of your manners and
the agreeableness of your conversation.

We often make a false estimate in preferring our or-
namental talents to our useful ones.

FABLE XLVI

The Mice in Council

Not urged by vain ambition's *airy dreams,*
Or specious wit, *does* wisdom *form her schemes,*
Poise well the scales, with due reflection *scan*
The means proposed, *and then adopt a plan.*

THE Mice called a General Council; and,
having met, after the doors were locked,
entered into a free consultation about ways and
means how to render their fortunes and estates
more secure from the danger of the Cat. Many
things were offered, and much was debated, *pro*
and *con*, upon the matter. At last a young Mouse,

in a fine florid speech, concluded upon an expedient, and that the only one, which was to put
them, for the future, entirely out of the power
of the enemy: and this was, that the Cat should
wear a bell about her neck, which upon the least
motion would give the alarm, and be a signal
for them to retire into their holes. This speech
was received with great applause, and it was even
proposed by some, that the Mouse who made it
should have the thanks of the assembly. Upon
which, an old grave Mouse, who had sat silent
all the while, stood up, and in another speech,
owned that the contrivance was admirable, and
the author of it, without doubt, an ingenious
Mouse; but, he said, he thought it would not
be so proper to vote him thanks, till he should
farther inform them how this bell was to be
fastened about the Cat's neck, and what Mouse
would undertake to do it.

*The different lights, in which things appear to different
    judgments, recommend candour to the opinions of
    others, even at the time we retain our own.*

Fable xlvii

The Old Man and Death

"Oh with what joy would I resign my breath!"
The wretch exclaims, and prays for instant death:
The fiend approaching, he inverts his pray'r,
"Oh grant me life, and double all my care!"

A POOR feeble old man, who had crawled out into a neighbouring wood to gather a few sticks, had made up his bundle, and, laying it over his shoulders, was trudging homeward with it; but, what with age, and the length of the way, and the weight of his burden, he grew so faint and weak that he sunk under it; and, as

he sat on the ground, called upon Death to come,
once for all, and ease him of his troubles. Death
no sooner heard him, but he came and demanded
of him what he wanted. The poor old creature,
who little thought Death had been so near, and
frightened almost out of his senses with his terrible aspect, answered him trembling: That having
by chance let his bundle of sticks fall, and being
too infirm to get it up himself, he had made bold
to call upon him to help him; that, indeed, this
was all he wanted at present; and that he hoped
his Worship was not offended with him for the
liberty he had taken in so doing.

*Men under calamity may seem to wish for death; but
they seldom bid him welcome when he stares them
in the face.*

FABLE XLVIII

The Crow and the Pitcher

When frowning *fates thy sanguine* hopes *defeat*,
And virtuous aims with disappointment *meet*,
Submit not to despair, *th' attempt renew*,
And rise superior *to the* vulgar *crew*.

A CROW, ready to die with thirst, flew with
joy to a pitcher which he beheld at some
distance. When he came, he found water in it
indeed, but so near the bottom, that with all
his stooping and straining, he was not able to
reach it. Then he endeavoured to overturn the
pitcher, that so at least he might be able to get

a little of it; but his strength was not sufficient for this. At last, seeing some pebbles lie near the place, he cast them one by one into the pitcher; and thus, by degrees, raised the water up to the very brim, and satisfied his thirst.

What we cannot compass by force, we may by invention and industry.

FABLE XLIX
𝕿𝖍𝖊 𝕱𝖔𝖝 𝖆𝖓𝖉 𝖙𝖍𝖊 𝕲𝖗𝖆𝖕𝖊𝖘

Old maids who loathe the matrimonial state,
Poor rogues who laugh to scorn the rich and great,
Patriots who rail at placemen and at pow'r,
All, like sly Reynard, say "The Grapes are sour."

A FOX, very hungry, chanced to come into a
Vineyard, where there hung many bunches
of charming ripe grapes; but nailed up to a trellis
so high, that he leaped till he quite tired himself without being able to reach one of them. At
last, Let who will take them! says he; they are
but green and sour; so I'll even let them alone.

When a man finds it impossible to obtain the things
he longs for, it is a mark of sound wisdon and
discretion to make a virtue of necessity.

FABLE L

The Viper and the File

Witlings! beware, nor wantonly provoke
Those who with int'rest may repay the joke;
Some claim our pity who fall preys to wit,
But all men triumph o'er the Biter Bit.

A VIPER entering a smith's shop, looked up and down for something to eat, and seeing a File, fell to gnawing it as greedily as could be. The File told him, very gruffly, that he had best be quiet and let him alone; for that he would get very little by nibbling at one, who, upon occasion, could bite iron and steel.

It's the fate of envy to attack those characters that are superior to its malice.

FABLE LI

The Mountains in Labour

Thus the vain Alchymist, in promise bold,
Beholds projection big with MINES *of* GOLD:
But now, his glasses burst, he thinks him rich
To save a little oil to cure the itch.

THE Mountains were said to be in labour,
and uttered most dreadful groans. People
came together, far and near, to see what birth
would be produced; and after they had waited
a considerable time in expectation, out crept a
mouse.

To raise uncommon expectations renders an ordinary
event ridiculous.

FABLE LII

𝕿𝖍𝖊 𝕿𝖜𝖔 𝕱𝖗𝖔𝖌𝖘

On things of moment *with thyself debate,*
Nor, inconsiderate, change *thy present state,*
Nor on the specious good *lay too much stress,*
Lest greater *Ills incur, in shunning* less.

O NE hot sultry summer, the lakes and ponds
being almost everywhere dried up, a couple
of Frogs agreed to travel together in search of
water. At last they came to a deep well, and
sitting upon the brink of it, began to consult,
whether they should leap in or no. One of them
was for it; urging, that there was plenty of clear

spring water, and no danger of being disturbed.
Well, says t'other, all this may be true; and yet
I can't come into your opinion for my life: For, if
the water should happen to dry up here too, how
should we get out again?

*We ought never to change our situation in life, without
duly considering the consequences of such a change.*

FABLE LIII

𝕿𝖍𝖊 𝕿𝖍𝖎𝖊𝖋 𝖆𝖓𝖉 𝖙𝖍𝖊 𝕯𝖔𝖌

Faithful *to* man, *and to thy conscience* just,
Spurn *him who* tempts *thee to* betray *thy trust.*
An honest mind's *the choicest gift of* heav'n,
How blest *to whom th'* etherial spark *is given!*

A THIEF coming to rob a certain house in the
night, was disturbed in his attempts by a
fierce vigilant dog who kept barking at him
continually. Upon which the thief, thinking to
stop his mouth, threw him a piece of bread: But
the dog refused it with indignation; telling him,
that before, he only suspected him to be a bad

man; but now, upon his offering to bribe him,
he was confirmed in his opinion; and that, as he
was entrusted with the guardianship of his master's house, he should never cease barking while
such a rogue as he lay lurking about it.

*Nothing can alter the honest purposes of the man, who
despises an insidious bribe; and whose mind is
proof against temptation.*

FABLE LIV

Hercules and the Carter

Inactive wishes are but waste of time,
And, without efforts, pray'rs themselves a crime:
Vain are their hopes who miracles expect,
And ask from heaven what themselves neglect.

AS a clownish fellow was driving his Cart along a deep miry lane, the wheels stuck so fast in the clay, that the horses could not draw them out. Upon this, he fell a bawling and praying to *Hercules* to come and help him. *Hercules* looking down from a cloud, bid him not lie there, like an idle rascal as he was, but get up and whip

his horses stoutly, and clap his shoulder to the
wheel, adding, That this was the only way for
him to obtain his assistance.

*Prayers and wishes amount to nothing: We must put
forth our own honest endeavours to obtain success
on the assistance of heaven.*

FABLE LV

The Sick Kite

Thus early sinning, and repenting late,
The dying debauchee would bribe his fate;
Pray'rs, alms, and promises he tries in vain,
Not sick of follies past, but present pain.

A KITE had been sick a long time; and finding there were no hopes of recovery, begged of his mother to go to all the churches and religious houses in the country, to try what prayers and promises would effect in his behalf. The old Kite replied: Indeed, dear Son, I would willingly undertake anything to save your life, but I have

great reason to despair of doing you any service
in the way you propose: For, with what face can
I ask anything of the Gods in favour of one whose
whole life has been a continued scene of rapine
and injustice, and who has not scrupled upon
occasion to rob the very altars themselves?

*After a long life spent in acts of impiety and wickedness,
we may justly suspect the sincerity of a death-bed
repentance.*

Fable lvi

The Two Pots

Born to the comforts of an humble state,
Fly their embrace, if courted by the great,
Happy to learn, how ill you can afford
The vast expense of how-d'yes from my lord.

AN earthen pot and one of brass, standing together upon the river's brink, were both
carried away by the flowing in of the tide. The
earthen pot showed some uneasiness, as fearing
he should be broken; but his companion of brass
bid him be under no apprehensions, for that he
would take care of him. Oh! replies the other,

keep as far off as ever you can, I entreat you; it
is you I am most afraid of: For, whether the
stream dashes you against me, or me against you,
I am sure to be the sufferer; and therefore, I beg
of you, do not let us come near one another.

*Reciprocal pleasure and advantage is the only rational
foundation for real friendship.*

FABLE LVII

𝕿𝖍𝖊 𝕾𝖕𝖆𝖗𝖗𝖔𝖜 𝖆𝖓𝖉 𝖙𝖍𝖊 𝕳𝖆𝖗𝖊

Tradesman, insult not, if a neighbour fail,
Lest, by and by, yourself should go to jail;
Nor, if a damsel slip, Prude, shake your head,
Lest you yourself next month be brought to bed.

A HARE, being seized by an Eagle, squeaked
out in a most woful manner. A Sparrow
that sat upon a tree just by and saw it, could not
forbear being unseasonably witty, but called out,
and said to the Hare: So ho! what! sit there and
be killed? Pr'ythee, up and away; I dare say, if
you would but try, so swift a creature as you are

would easily escape from the Eagle. As he was going on with his cruel raillery, down came a Hawk, and snapt him up; and, notwithstanding his vain cries and lamentations, fell a devouring of him in an instant. The Hare, who was just expiring, yet received comfort from this accident, even in the agonies of death; and, addressing her last words to the Sparrow, said: You, who just now insulted my misfortune with so much security, as you thought, may please to shew us how well you can bear the like, now it has befallen you.

The mutability of human affairs is such, that no situation, however seemingly advantageous, ought to make us jest with the misfortunes of others.

FABLE LVIII

𝕿𝖍𝖊 𝕮𝖆𝖙 𝖆𝖓𝖉 𝖙𝖍𝖊 𝕱𝖔𝖝

The sly politician may boast of his arts,
How his budget is full, and by cunning he's guided;
But the wise and the wary, less proud of his parts,
With a single expedient is better provided.

AS the Cat and the Fox were talking politics
together, on a time, in the middle of the
forest, *Reynard* said, Let things turn out ever so
bad, he did not care, for he had a thousand tricks
for them yet before they should hurt him. But
pray, says he, Mrs. Puss, suppose there should
be an invasion, what course do you design to

take? Nay, says the Cat, I have but one shift
for it; and if that won't do, I am undone. I am
sorry for you, replies *Reynard*, with all my heart,
and would gladly furnish you with one or two
of mine, but indeed, neighbour, as times go, it
is not good to trust; we must even be every one
for himself, as the saying is, and so your humble
servant. These words were scarce out of his
mouth, when they were alarmed with a pack of
hounds that came upon them full cry. The Cat,
by the help of her single shift, ran up a tree, and
sat securely among the top branches; from
whence she beheld *Reynard*, who had not been
able to get out of sight, overtaken with his thousand tricks, and torn in as many pieces by the
dogs which had surrounded him.

*Successful cunning often makes an ostentatious preten-
sion to wisdom.*

Fable lix

The Old Hound

Oh let not those whom honest servants bless,
With cruel hand their age infirm oppress;
Forget their service past, their former truth,
And all the cares and labours of their youth.

AN old Hound, who had been an excellent good one in his time, and given his master great sport and satisfaction in many a chase, at last, by the effect of years, became feeble and unserviceable. However, being in the field one day, when the Stag was almost run down, he happened to be the first that came in with him, and seized him by one of his haunches; but, his decayed and broken teeth not being able to keep their hold, the Deer escaped, and threw him quite out. Upon which, his master, being in a great passion, was going to strike him, when the honest old creature is said to have barked out his apology: Ah! do not strike your poor old servant; it is not my heart and inclination, but my strength and speed that fail me. If what I now am displeases, pray don't forget what I have been.

Useful services, performed in youth, ought not to be cancelled by old age and infirmities.

Fable LX

Two Young Men and the Cook

Thus quibbling thieves evade the charge,
Offend the laws, and go at large:
But though 'tis hard the crime to fix,
We know they're guilty by their tricks.

TWO young men went into a cook's shop,
under pretence of buying meat; and while
the cook's back was turned, one of them snatched
up a piece of beef, and gave it to his companion,
who presently clapt it under his cloak. The cook
turning about again, and missing his beef, began
to charge them with it; upon which, he that first

took it swore bitterly he had none of it. He that had it swore as heartily, that he had taken up none of his meat. Why look ye, gentlemen, says the cook, I see your equivocation; and though I can't tell which of you has taken my meat, I am sure, between you both, there's a thief, and a couple of rascals.

Evading the truth is just as blameable as denying it.

FABLE LXI

The Dog and the Sheep

Whose life is safe, if tried before a judge,
That to the hapless pris'ner bears a grudge?
Whose property secur'd from lawless fury,
If any private int'rest warps the jury?

THE Dog sued the Sheep for a debt, of which the Kite and the Wolf were to be judges. They, without debating long upon the matter, or making any scruple for want of evidence, gave sentence for the plaintiff; who immediately tore the poor Sheep in pieces, and divided the spoil with the unjust judges.

We cannot reasonably hope for justice in a court, where
the judges are interested in the decision.

FABLE LXII

The Proud Frog

Ye cits! of narrow means and small estate,
View not with envy the luxurious great:
Think that from riot bankruptcies will come,
And mark your prudent neighbour worth a plum.

AN Ox, grazing in a meadow, chanced to set his foot among a parcel of young frogs, and trod one of them to death. The rest informed their mother, when she came home, what had happened; telling her, that the beast which did it was the hugest creature that ever they saw in their lives. What, was it so big? says the old

Frog, swelling and blowing up her speckled belly
to a great degree. Oh, bigger by a vast deal, say
they. And so big? says she, straining herself yet
more. Indeed, Mamma, say they, if you were to
burst yourself, you would never be so big. She
strove yet again, and burst herself indeed.

*The silly ambition of vying with our superiors, in
station and fortune, is the direct road to ruin.*

FABLE LXIII

The Dove and the Bee

Hail gratitude! the spark whence virtue springs,
And adoration to the King of kings;
The greatest bliss the feeling bosom knows,
The source whence every gen'rous action flows.

THE Bee, compelled by thirst, went to drink
in a clear purling rivulet; but the current,
with its circling eddy, snatched her away, and
carried her down the stream. A Dove, pitying
her distressed condition, cropt a branch from a
neighbouring tree, and let it fall into the water,
by means of which the Bee saved herself, and got

ashore. Not long after, a Fowler, having a design
upon the Dove, planted his nets and all his little
artillery in due order, without the Bird's observing what he was about; which the Bee perceiving, just as he was going to put his design in
execution she bit him by the heel, and made him
give so sudden a start, that the Dove took the
alarm, and flew away.

*Charity will have its rewards one time or other; for
certain in the promised recompense hereafter, perhaps in a grateful return here.*

FABLE LXIV

The Collier and the Fuller

With vice allied, however pure,
No virtue can be long secure:
Shun then the traitress and her wiles,
Whate'er she touches she defiles.

THE Collier and the Fuller, being old ac-
quaintance, happened upon a time to meet
together; and the latter, being but ill provided
with a habitation, was invited by the former to
come and live in the same house with him. I
thank you, my dear friend, replies the Fuller, for
your kind offer, but it cannot be; for if I were

to dwell with you, whatever I should take pains
to scour and make clean in the morning, the dust
of you and your coals would blacken and defile,
as bad as ever, before night.

*We commonly imbibe the principles and manners of
those with whom we associate.*

FABLE LXV

The Boy and his Mother

Fathers and mothers! train your children's youth
To virtue, honour, honesty, and truth;
Dreadful! to bring about your child's damnation,
And give your sons a Tyburn *education.*

A LITTLE Boy, who went to school, stole one of his school-fellow's horn-books, and brought it home to his mother; who was so far from correcting and discouraging him upon account of the theft, that she commended and gave him an apple for his pains. In process of time, as the child grew up to be a man, he accustomed himself to greater robberies; and at last, being apprehended and committed to gaol, he was tried and condemned for a felony. On the day of his execution, as the officers were conducting him to the gallows, he was attended by a vast crowd of people, and among the rest by his mother, who came sighing and sobbing along, and deploring extremely her son's unhappy fate; which the criminal observing, he called to the sheriff, and begged the favour of him, that he would give him leave to speak a word or two to his poor afflicted mother. The sheriff (as who would deny a dying man so reasonable a request) gave him permission; and the felon, while every one thought he was whispering something of importance to his mother, bit off her ear, to the great offence and surprise of the whole assembly. What, say they, was not this villain contented with the impious acts which he has already committed, but he must increase the number of them, by doing this violence to his mother? Good people, replied he, I would not have you be under a mistake; that wicked woman deserves this, and even worse at my hands; for if she had chastised and chid, instead of rewarding and caressing me, when in my infancy I stole the horn-book from the school, I had not come to this ignominious untimely end.

Youthful minds, like the pliant wax, are susceptible of the most lasting impressions, and the good or evil bias they then receive is seldom or ever eradicated.

FABLE LXVI

The Wanton Calf

Thus oft the industrious poor endures reproach
From rogues in lace, and sharpers in a coach;
But soon to Tyburn *sees the villains led,*
While he still earns in peace his daily bread.

A CALF, full of play and wantonness, seeing
the Ox at plough, could not forbear in-
sulting him. What a sorry poor drudge art thou,
says he, to bear that heavy yoke upon your neck,
and go all day drawing a plough at your tail, to
turn up the ground for your master! But you are
a wretched dull slave, and know no better, or

else you would not do it. See what a happy life I lead; I go just where I please; sometimes I lie down under the cool shade; sometimes frisk about in the open sunshine; and, when I please, slake my thirst in the clear sweet brook: But you, if you were to perish, have not so much as a little dirty water to refresh you. The Ox, not at all moved with what he said, went quietly and calmly on with his work: and, in the evening, was unyoked and turned loose. Soon after which he saw the Calf taken out of the field, and delivered into the hands of a priest, who immediately led him to the altar, and prepared to sacrifice him. His head was hung round with fillets of flowers, and the fatal knife was just going to be applied to his throat, when the Ox drew near and whispered him to this purpose: Behold the end of your insolence and arrogance; it was for this only you were suffered to live at all; and pray now, friend, whose condition is best, yours or mine?

To insult people in distress is the property of a cruel, indiscreet, and giddy temper; for on the next turn of fortune's wheel, we may be thrown down to their condition, and they exalted to ours.

FABLE LXVII

Jupiter and the Herdsman

Short-sighted wretch! endure thy care,
Nor heave th' impatient sigh:
Heav'n hears thee, but perhaps thy pray'r
'Tis mercy to deny.

A HERDSMAN, missing a young heifer that belonged to his herd, went up and down the forest to seek it. And having walked a great deal of ground to no purpose, he fell a praying to *Jupiter* for relief; promising to sacrifice a Kid to him, if he would help him to a discovery of the thief. After this, he went on a little farther, and came near a grove of oaks, where he found the carcase of his heifer, and a lion grumbling over it, and feeding upon it. This sight almost scared him out of his wits; so down he fell upon his knees once more, and addressing himself to *Jupiter;* O *Jupiter!* says he, I promised thee a Kid to show me the thief, but now I promise thee a bull, if thou wilt be so merciful as to deliver me out of his clutches.

We ought never to supplicate the Divine power, but through motives of religion and virtue; prayers, dictated by passion or interest, are unacceptable to the Deity.

FABLE LXVIII

𝕿𝖍𝖊𝖗𝖊'𝖘 𝖓𝖔 𝕿𝖔-𝖒𝖔𝖗𝖗𝖔𝖜

Eager *to mend*, *and* brookless *of delay*,
Sincere *repentance waits no* future *day;*
The present *moment only* is *allow'd;*
Uncertain *hopes and fears* to-morrow *shroud*.

A MAN, who had lived a very profligate life,
at length being awakened by the lively
representations of a sober friend on the apprehensions of a feverish indisposition, promised
that he would heartily set about his reformation,
and that To-morrow he would seriously begin it.
But the symptoms going off, and that To-morrow

coming, he still put it off till the next, and so he went on from one To-morrow to another; but still he continued his reprobate life. This his friend observing, said to him, I am very much concerned to find how little effect my disinterested advice has upon you: But, my friend, let me tell you, that since your To-morrow never comes, nor do you seem to intend it shall, I will believe you no more, except you set about your repentance and amendment this very moment: for, to say nothing of your repeated broken promises, you must consider, that the time that is past is no more; that To-morrow is *not* OURS; and the *present* NOW is all we have to boast off.

That compunction of heart cannot be sincere, which takes not immediate effect, and can be put off till To-morrow. The friend's closing observation in the Fable is so good a moral, that we need add nothing to it.

A NOTE ON
THE ILLUSTRATOR

THOMAS BEWICK was born in 1753 in Northumberland, England. He was one of eight children and spent his boyhood on his father's farm. As a boy he was a precocious and prolific artist, filling the margins of his schoolbooks with drawings of beasts and birds. At fourteen he was apprenticed to an engraver of ornamental silver and stationery. Here he was soon called on to cut wood engravings for local printers. He tried working in London for awhile but soon returned to Northumberland where he opened a shop.

Here, for over fifty years, he worked with his brother John and a succession of employees and students to produce the wood engravings that set the pattern for book illustration for a century to come. Besides the intrinsic beauty of the work of Bewick and his school there was the skill and rightness of his technique. Before Bewick most engravers worked with a knife on the softer side of the wood cutting away the unwanted areas. He chose instead the discipline of working with a graver on the hard end grain. This permitted meticulous detail and varying effects of distance and tone.

Bewick died in 1828 at the age of 75 and is buried in a churchyard across the river from Cherryburn House where he was born.

G.H.